STARS OF
DESTINY

A SCIENTIFIC LOOK
AT ASTROLOGY

PATRICK MOORE

CANOPUS PUBLISHING LIMITED

© Canopus Publishing Limited 2005

First published in 2005 by Canopus Publishing Limited
27 Queen Square, Bristol BS1 4ND, UK

The moral right of the author has been asserted

A catalogue record for this book is available from the British Library
ISBN 0 9537868 6 2

Constellation maps by Paul Doherty
New zodiac drawings by Roger Prout
Project editor: Julian Brigstocke
Proofreader: John Adamson
Printed and bound in Great Britain by Short Run Press

CONTENTS

Acknowledgements

My grateful thanks are due to Roger Prout, FRAS, for illustrating my new Zodiac, and to Keith Newbery and all at the *Chichester Observer* for publishing my star-sign questionnaire.

Patrick Moore
Selsey, August 2004

Chapter 1

INTRODUCTION

One morning in June 2001 I had a distinct surprise. Having finished my third cup of breakfast coffee, I opened my daily paper and read that the University of Southampton, one of the best-known educational establishments in the British Isles, was to form a research group for a critical study of astrology. According to the report, the students were setting out to 'investigate the links between the planets and various aspects of human behaviour'. The project was to be led by Professor Christopher Bagley, of the university's Faculty of Social Sciences.

Frankly I was incredulous. I knew that there had been various precedents; the Sorbonne in Paris had considered awarding a doctorate to Elizabeth Teissier, who had already given President Mitterand advice on matters of state, but public opinion insisted that the doctorate should be given for sociology rather than astrology. Several political leaders were known to have been astrology-minded, notably President Chirac of France. (Ronald Reagan is often linked with astrology, but had no personal belief in it – I know, because I asked him.) And, of course, astrology is immensely powerful in backward countries. But I could not believe that Southampton University could be involved, so I wrote to find out.

The situation was much as I had expected. The newspaper report was based on the activities of the university's Social Work Studies department, and was causing 'considerable embarrassment and annoyance' to the Department of Physics and Astronomy. Professor Malcolm Coe was quite definite: 'Needless to say, our department has nothing to do with such "astrological studies", and is certainly not offering degrees in astrology'. But is there any justification for regarding astrology as a subject to be taken seriously?

Even in the year 2004, there are still many people in the Western world who believe in astrology, or at least feel that there may be 'something in it'. There are also many astrologers, both professional and amateur, and the professionals take themselves very seriously indeed; they hold meetings, they organise full scale conventions, and they solemnly give each other 'degrees', such as D.F.Astrol.S. and F.Astrol.Soc. Many of them are quite sincere, and look down with scorn on the tabloid-newspaper columnists and the professors who operate from seaside piers. A D.F.Astrol.S. will curl his lip and sneer at the very mention of a dark lady coming over the water.

Thousands of new books on astrology are published every year, and it is natural to ask whether there is room for another. My justification is that I am approaching the whole subject in a very definite way, and I am not setting out to write anything in the nature of a comprehensive review; if you have the time and inclination to cast a horoscope, refer to a suitable book, such as *The New Complete Astrologer* by Derek and Julia Parker (Crescent Books, New York, 2000).

All I hope to do is to see whether it is possible to answer just two questions:

1. Is there any scientific basis for astrology?
2. Does it work – and if so, why?

I do not propose to stray into the mad domain of flying saucers, little green men from Mars, and visitors from Outer Space; I leave that to others. I will keep to science, not fantasy. If the answers to my two fundamental questions are (1) No and (2) No, there is no need to waste any more time on the astrologers. If the answers are Yes and Yes, or even Maybe and Maybe, we must think again!

CHAPTER 2

THE REVOLVING HEAVENS

It was natural for early peoples to believe that the Earth must be all-important, lying at rest in the exact centre of the universe with the sky revolving round it once in twenty-four hours. Even when it was realised that the Earth is a globe rather than a flat plane, it still retained its proud central position, from which it was not finally dislodged until less than 400 years ago.

In fact the Earth is a planet nearly 8000 miles in diameter, moving round the Sun at a distance of 93 million miles – very close indeed on the astronomical scale. There are eight other planets, moving round the Sun at various distances in various periods, and these, together with minor bodies such as satellites, comets and meteoroids, make up what is called the Solar System.

The Sun itself is an ordinary star, and looks so splendid in our skies only because it is, cosmically speaking, on our doorstep. The other stars are suns in their own right, but are millions of millions of miles away, so that their movements relative to each other are too slow to be noticed with the naked eye over periods of many lifetimes. They were once termed the 'fixed stars'.

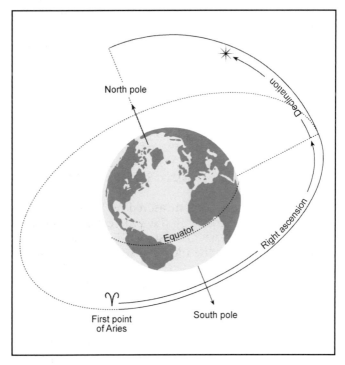

Celestial sphere. Equatorial coordinates give star positions based on Earth's equator. Courtesy James Symonds.

Our ancestors had no idea of the real nature of the universe, and they believed the sky to be solid, with the stars attached to it in the manner of tiny lamps. Yet they could, and did, make accurate measurements, and they drew up what is still called the celestial sphere – an imaginary sphere whose centre coincides with the centre of the Earth, as shown in the diagram.

Northward, the Earth's axis of rotation points to the north pole of the sky, at present very close to the brightish star Polaris in the constellation of Ursa Minor (the Little Bear). As the Earth spins, Polaris seems to stay still, with everything else – including the Sun – moving round it. Just as the Earth's equator divides the world into two hemispheres, so the celestial equator cuts the sky into two hemispheres. If you go to the North Pole, you will see Polaris overhead, whilst the celestial equator will lie along the horizon. Go to the South Pole, and the equator will still lie along the horizon; Polaris will never be seen – it will be directly below your feet – and the south celestial pole, unfortunately unmarked by any bright star, will be overhead.

On Earth, positions are measured by latitude (angular distance north or south of the equator) and longitude (angular distance east or west of the prime meridian, arbitrarily chosen as the meridian which passes through both poles and Greenwich Observatory in Outer London). The celestial equivalents are called declination and right ascension; thus Polaris has declination of almost 90 degrees N., while stars on the celestial equator are at declination 0 degrees. Because the stars are so nearly 'fixed', their right ascensions and declinations do not alter much, but there is one all-important phenomenon which affects both astronomy and astrology. This is precession.

Because the Earth completes one orbit of the Sun in one year, the Sun seems to move right round the sky once a year; its apparent path against the stars is called the ecliptic. Of course the Sun and the stars cannot be seen at the same time – the sky is too bright – but it is easy to calculate just where the Sun will be at any one moment. The ecliptic is tilted to the celestial equator by an angle of 23.5 degrees, and so during its yearly journey the Sun crosses the equator twice, once when moving from south to north in March (the vernal equinox, or First Point of Aries), and once when moving from north to south in September (the autumnal equinox, or First Point of Libra).

At the moment, Polaris is within one degree of the north celestial pole, but it has not always been so. As the Earth spins, it 'wobbles' very slightly in the manner of a gyroscope which is running down, and has started to topple. This wobble is very slow, and takes 26,000 years to complete a cycle, as shown in the next diagram, but it does mean that the position of the celestial pole alters, and when the Egyptian Pyramids were being built the pole star was the relatively faint Thuban, in the constellation of the Dragon. I will have more to say about this later.

At a fairly early stage in the story of civilisation, it was realised that the planets, star-like though they look, behave in a very unstellar way. They wander around, though they do keep within certain well-defined zones to either side of the ecliptic. Five planets were known in ancient times: Mercury, Venus, Mars, Jupiter and Saturn – the Latin names for the Greek gods. Three more, Uranus, Neptune and Pluto, have been found since: Uranus in 1781, Neptune in 1846 and Pluto as recently as 1930. The changing positions of the Sun, Moon and planets against the starry background provide the whole basis for astrology.

promptly raised an army, invaded his father's domain, and had Ulugh Beigh murdered. That was one astrological prediction which came true, and it also marked the end of the Arab school of astronomy.

Astrology continued to flourish even after the invention of the telescope, in the opening decade of the seventeenth century, but gradually its influence waned. Probably the last great astronomer who believed implicitly in astrology was no less a person than Sir Isaac Newton, whose *Principia*, published in 1689, finally proved that the Sun, not the Earth, is the central body of the Solar System. Thereafter astrology became less and less influential in the Western world, and by now there is no leading astronomer who has any faith in it.

Things were – and are – different in the East. In 1971 the then Indian Prime Minister, Mrs Indira Gandhi, timed the date of the General Election on astrological advice, winning it easily. There was a strange episode in Thailand in 1991, when the General Election there was brought forward on the recommendation of the astrologers, with the result that the main opposition party was given no time to prepare, so that its candidates were excluded!

Astrology has had many famous supporters, such as the educational eccentric Rudolf Steiner (who also believed the Earth to be flat) and a good many eminent psychiatrists. But astrology and astronomy have gone their separate ways. They are as different as the proverbial chalk and the equally proverbial cheese.

CHAPTER 3

NEIGHBOURS

To set the scene, I must say something about 'pure astronomy'. We are concerned with our near neighbours, the members of the Solar System, and their movements against the backcloth of stars. I will make no attempt to give a conventional account; instead I will merely concentrate on those aspects which are directly relevant to my main theme. Can the bodies in the Solar System have any effect upon us?

Obviously the answer so far as the Sun and the Moon are concerned is 'yes' – you don't need an astrologer to point that out! We owe everything to the Sun; without it the Earth would never have come into existence. Our world was born in a cloud of dust and gas surrounding the youthful Sun, around 4600 million years ago. Since then there may have been variations in the output of solar energy, and these may well have been the main cause of the Ice Ages which have occurred periodically; the last Ice Age ended a mere 10,000 years ago. But all things considered, the Sun is a steady, well-behaved star, and it is not likely to change drastically for well over 1000 million years in the future.

The Sun is large. Its diameter is 865,000 miles, so that it could comfortably swallow up more than a million globes the volume of the Earth. It is also very massive, and it is extremely hot. The surface temperature is not far short of 6000 degrees Celsius, and near the centre of the globe, where the energy is being produced, the temperature rockets to the unbelievable value of around 15 million degrees.

It was only around sixty years ago that astronomers found out just how the Sun shines; before that there had been many different theories, some of which sounded convincing while others were very wide of the mark. It seems natural to assume that the Sun is simply burning in the manner of a coal fire, but a very quick calculation shows that this cannot be the answer. A Sun made up entirely of coal, and radiating as fiercely as the Sun actually does, would turn to ashes in a few million years, and the Sun is a great deal older than that; it must be older than the Earth, so that its age is of the order of 5000 million years. Even so, it is no more than half-way through its luminous career.

The Sun shines by nuclear reactions. The main 'fuel' is hydrogen, which is the most common substance in the universe (the numbers of hydrogen atoms exceed those of all the other elements put together). The Sun contains a vast amount of hydrogen, and near the centre of the globe, where the temperatures and pressures are colossal, strange things are happening. Hydrogen atoms (or, more precisely, the nuclei of hydrogen atoms) are combining to

build up nuclei of the second lightest element, helium.
The process is going on all the time, and each time a new
helium nucleus is formed a little energy is set free and a
little mass (or weight, if you like) is lost. It is this energy
which keeps the Sun shining. The mass-loss amounts
to 4 million tons per second, but by solar standards
this is negligible.

The Earth's orbit round the Sun is not very different
from a circle. The distance ranges between
91.5 million miles at perihelion out to 94.5 million miles
at aphelion, so that if I drew a scale diagram of the orbit
on a page of this book it would be difficult to tell that the
shape is slightly elliptical. Actually we are closest to the
Sun in December and furthest out in June; our seasons are
due to the 23.5 degree tilt of the Earth's axis relative to
our path round the Sun.

So far as we are concerned, our satellite, the Moon, is
the most important body in the sky apart from the Sun.
In itself it is very insignificant; it is only just over
2000 miles in diameter, and if you put the Earth into one
pan of a gigantic pair of scales you would need 81 Moons
to balance it. But it is very close; its mean distance from
us is a mere 239,000 miles, and it stays together with us
in our never-ending journey round the Sun. Brilliant
though it may look, it has no light of its own, and
depends entirely upon reflecting the rays of the Sun. This
is why it shows phases, or apparent changes in shape,
from new to full.

The diagram will, I hope, make this clear. It is not to
scale – the Sun is 400 times further away than the Moon
– but this does not matter for the moment. In position,
the Moon is between the Earth and the Sun; its dark side
is turned toward us, and we cannot see the Moon at all
except on the rare occasions when the alignment is

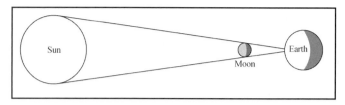

Solar eclipse. The shadow cast by the Moon can just touch the Earth. This diagram is not to scale! Courtesy James Symonds.

perfect, so that the Moon passes right in front of the Sun to produce a solar eclipse. This, not the slender crescent seen in the evening sky, is the true new moon.

The Moon takes 27.3 days to complete one orbit. As it moves along from the bottom position, it appears first as a crescent, then as a half (first quarter) and then as a three-quarter or waxing gibbous shape before reaching the top position, when we see the whole of the sunlit hemisphere; the Moon is full, and opposite to the Sun in the sky. It may sometimes pass into the shadow cast by the Earth, and since the supply of direct sunlight is temporarily cut off, the Moon turns a dim, often coppery colour until it passes out of the shadow again; this is termed a lunar eclipse. The phases are then repeated in reverse order; waning gibbous, half (last quarter) and back to new. Because the Earth and the Moon are moving together round the Sun, the interval between one new moon and the next (or one full moon and the next) is 29.5 days rather than only 27.3 days.

The Moon's path round the Earth is not quite circular. At its closest to us (perigee) it is slightly less than 230,000 miles away, and at its furthest (apogee) just over 250,000 miles. But this is not linked with the phases; the Moon is not necessarily at perigee when full. For example, in December 2001 the Moon was at perigee on

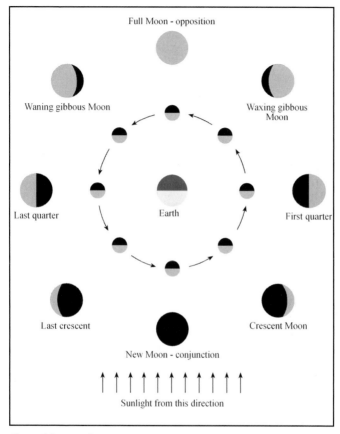

Phases of the Moon, from new (conjunction) to full. Courtesy James Symonds.

the 6th of the month and full on the 30th.

Because the Moon is so much smaller than the Earth, as well as being less dense, its pull of gravity is much weaker than ours. Go there, as the Apollo astronauts have done, and you will have only one-sixth of your Earth weight. One very important result of this feeble pull is that the Moon has virtually no atmosphere.

If you throw an object upward, it will rise to a certain height and then fall back to earth. Throw it faster, and it will rise higher. If you could throw it up at a speed of 7 miles per second, or roughly 25,000 miles per hour, it would never come down at all; the Earth's gravity would not be strong enough to draw it back, and the object would escape into space. Therefore, 7 miles per second is the Earth's 'escape velocity', and this is high enough for us to retain a dense atmosphere. The air we breathe is made up of myriads of particles, all flying around, but they cannot attain a speed of 7 miles per second, and so they cannot escape. On the Moon, however, the escape velocity is only 1.5 miles per second, and this is not enough; any atmosphere the Moon may once have had has long since leaked away into space, and by now there is so little left that if we call the Moon 'an airless world' we are to all intents and purposes correct. If it is airless, it must also be waterless and lifeless.

The lunar surface is rugged and mountainous. There are broad lava-plains, miscalled 'seas', and there are thousands upon thousands of craters, produced when the Moon was subjected to a natural bombardment by rocky particles from space. This bombardment ended over 1000 million years ago, and since then the Moon has known no major activity. No life existed there before Neil Armstrong and Buzz Aldrin, from Apollo 11, touched down in July 1969.

The Moon spins on its axis; the rotation period is the same as the orbital period: 27.3 days. There is no mystery about this. Tidal effects over the ages have been responsible, and it means that the Moon keeps the same

Craters of the Moon. I took this photograph in 1999 with my 15-inch reflector. The dark-floored crater is Plato, 60 miles in diameter; the Sirius Iridyum (Bay of Rainbows) is to the right. The upper part of the picture shows part of the Mare Imbrium (Sea of Showers).

hemisphere turned toward us all the time. Before the Russians sent a probe, Lunik 3, on a 'round trip' in 1959, we had no direct knowledge about the averted hemisphere, which from Earth we cannot see. It proved to be just as mountainous, just as cratered, and just as lifeless as the side we have always known. By now, of course, the entire lunar surface has been mapped in detail.

The Moon is the main cause of the ocean tides, and so has a tremendous effect upon all life – not only aquatic life. But what about the planets?

It is immediately obvious that the Solar System is divided into two well-marked parts. First we have four relatively small, solid planets: Mercury to Mars. Beyond Mars there is a wide gap in which move thousands of dwarf worlds known as minor planets or asteroids, and then come the four giants (Jupiter to Neptune), plus Pluto, which does not seem to fit into the general system and may not be worthy of true planetary status. The relevant details are summarised in the table.

No, there is no mistake in the table, Pluto has a very eccentric orbit, and may at times be closer-in than Neptune, as it was between 1979 and 1999.

What we must decide is whether any of the planets, on their own, can have any detectable effects upon life on the Earth. As a start, it will help to say a little about each of the planets in turn, though I am again confining myself to facts which may (or may not!) have a bearing on my main theme.

Planet	Mean Distance from Sun (millions of miles)	Orbital Period	Minimum Distance from Earth (millions of miles)	Diameter (miles)	Mass (Earth = 1)
Mercury	36	88 days	48	3030	0.06
Venus	67	225 days	24.4	7523	0.81
Earth	93	365 days	–	7926	1
Mars	141.5	687 days	34	4222	0.2
Jupiter	483	11.9 years	365	89,424	318
Saturn	886	29.5 years	740	74,914	95
Uranus	1783	84.0 years	1604	31,600	15
Neptune	2793	165.8 years	2674	31,410	17
Pluto	3666	247.7 years	2382	1444	0.002

Mercury is never very conspicuous, simply because it always lies in the same part of the sky as the Sun, and is visible with the naked eye only when very low in the west after sunset or very low in the east before sunrise. It shows phases of the same basic type as those of the Moon, though of course you need a good telescope to see them. Mercury has a weak gravitational pull, and a weak but definite magnetic field. There is virtually no atmosphere, so that life there is out of the question. One unmanned space-craft has passed by it (Mariner 10, in 1974–5), and sent back pictures of a rough, cratered landscape not unlike that of the Moon, though with important differences in detail. Another probe (Messenger) was launched in 2004, but will travel by a roundabout route, and will not begin to orbit Mercury until 2011.

Venus is the brightest object in the sky apart from the Sun and the Moon; at its best it can cast shadows. In size and mass it is almost a twin of the Earth, but, unlike our world, it has no detectable magnetic field. Like Mercury, it shows lunar-type phases. Telescopically, all that can be seen is a more or less featureless disk, either a crescent, half or gibbous (not full, because when its day side faces us it is on the far side of the Sun, and to all intents and purposes out of view). The actual surface is permanently hidden by a dense, cloud-laden atmosphere; there is no such thing as a sunny day on Venus. Various space-craft have been sent there, and have told us that the surface conditions are intensely hostile. The atmosphere is made up chiefly of the choking, unbreathable gas carbon dioxide, which acts in the manner of a greenhouse and shuts in the Sun's heat, so that the surface temperature is of the order of 500 degrees Celsius. There are mountains, lava-flows and huge volcanoes which are probably active. The clouds are rich in sulphuric acid, and the atmospheric pressure is 90 times that of our own air at sea-level. (I remember that in 1960 I gave a lecture in London, during which I said that as a potential colony Venus seemed more promising than Mars. How wrong I was!)

Venus: from Mariner 10, 5 February 1974. Only the upper clouds are shown; the surface is permanently cloud-shrouded. Courtesy NASA/JPL-Caltech.

Mars never comes as close as Venus, but at least it is less unlike the Earth than any other planet, though it is much smaller. Because it is further away from the Sun than we are, it does not show lunar-type phases, though at times it may appear decidedly gibbous. When at its best it can outshine all the planets apart from Venus, but when at its greatest distance from the Earth it looks like

Mars from Viking Orbiter. The Schiaparelli crater, which is 280 miles in diameter, can be seen at the centre. Courtesy USGS/NASA.

nothing more than a fairly bright red star. It has a thin atmosphere, made up mainly of carbon dioxide.

The poles are covered with white ice-caps, which wax and wane with the Martian seasons. Telescopes show a predominantly reddish surface, on which are darker patches which were once, wrongly, believed to be seas, or at least old sea-beds filled with vegetation; in fact they are areas where the red, dusty stuff has been blown away by winds in the thin atmosphere, exposing the darker rocks below. The red areas are usually called deserts, and this is not a bad name for them, but they are not similar to our Sahara; a Martian desert is coated with reddish minerals, and it is cold. On the equator at Martian midsummer the temperature may rise to around 40 degrees Fahrenheit, but the nights are bitter, because the atmosphere is very poor at retaining heat. A Martian 'day' amounts to 24 hours 37 minutes, and the seasons are of the same basic type as ours, apart from being much longer.

Many space-craft have been sent to Mars, and we have very good maps of the surface, showing mountains, craters, canyons and vast volcanoes which may or may not be extinct; one volcano, Olympus Mons, rises to a height of 15 miles above the surrounding surface, and is crowned by a caldera 40 miles in diameter.

We cannot yet be sure whether or not there is any trace of life on Mars. Space-craft have made controlled landings there, sampling the surface materials and sending back details of their findings, but so far there is no evidence of any living thing. Any organisms there must be very simple. There can be nothing so advanced as a blade of grass, and the 'Martians' of H.G. Wells and countless lesser writers must remain in the realm of science fiction. We will find out for certain when we can obtain samples from the planet and analyse them in our laboratories, something which should be possible within the next few years.

Mercury and Venus have no satellites. We have one – our faithful Moon – and Mars has two, Phobos and Deimos. However, both of these are true midgets, less than 20 miles across, and are certainly former asteroids which were captured by Mars long ago. Future colonists will find them of very little use in providing illumination during the dark Martian nights.

The main asteroid belt lies between the orbits of Mars and Jupiter. Only one member of the swarm, Ceres, is as much as 500 miles in diameter, and only one, Vesta, is ever visible with the naked eye. Most of the rest are tiny, all are airless and lifeless, with very weak gravitational pulls and, so far as we know, no magnetic fields. They are simply cosmical débris, left over, so to speak, when the main planets were formed from the solar nebula 4600 million years ago.

Some small asteroids have orbits which swing them away from the main belt, and bring them close to the Earth. It is always possible that one of these wanderers might collide with us, and there is a well-supported theory that this did happen some 65 million years ago, causing such a disturbance that the world's climate was completely changed – with disastrous results for the dinosaurs, which could not cope with the new conditions and died out. What can happen in the past can happen again. The chances of a dangerous impact are slight, but they are not nil, and careful watch is now being kept in order to trace these errant bodies. If we saw one on a collision course, we might possibly be able to divert it by means of a nuclear explosion, provided that we had enough time to prepare.

Jupiter, giant of the Sun's family, is more massive than all the other planets combined. Despite its great distance it is very brilliant, and is outshone only by Venus and, very occasionally, by Mars. Its huge globe could contain over 1300 bodies the volume of the Earth, but it is a world of a quite different type, and may be called a gas-giant. There seems to be a hot silicate core, surrounded by layers of liquid hydrogen which are in turn overlaid by the deep, hydrogen-rich atmosphere which we can see. Telescopes show a yellowish, flattened disk, crossed by

Jupiter. Imaged from the Hubble Space Telescope from a range of 519,000,000 miles. Courtesy Reta Beebe, Amy Simon (New Mexico State University) and NASA.

dark streaks known as cloud belts. There is a vast amount of detail, which is always changing; of special note is the Great Red Spot, a vast oval storm whose surface area is greater than that of the Earth. Though Jupiter has a long 'year', it is a quick spinner, and a Jovian 'day' amounts to less than ten hours, which is why the globe is so obviously flattened. There are several dark rings, quite unlike the glorious ring-system of Saturn.

Most of our detailed knowledge of Jupiter comes from

the space-craft which have been sent past it. We have found that the planet is surrounded by zones of lethal radiation, so that any astronaut incautious enough to venture too close would meet with a quick and unpleasant death. There is a very powerful magnetic field, far stronger than that of any other planet.

Of Jupiter's numerous satellites, four – Io, Europa, Ganymede and Callisto – are of planetary size, and any small telescope will show them. Ganymede and Callisto are icy and cratered, Europa icy and smooth, and Io violently volcanic, with eruptions going on all the time. All these four are larger than Pluto, and Ganymede is actually larger than Mercury, though not so massive.

Saturn, the outermost of the planets known in ancient times, is in some ways not too unlike Jupiter, but is less massive; its mean density is less than that of water – it has been said that if you could drop Saturn into a vast ocean, it would float! Like Jupiter, it is a quick spinner, so that the globe is obviously flattened; there are belts, less prominent than those of Jupiter, and occasional white spots. The rings are made up of swarms of ice particles, all whirling round the planet in the manner of dwarf moons. Whether they represent the débris of a former icy satellite which ventured too close-in, and was broken up by Saturn's powerful pull of gravity, or whether they are simply material which never condensed into a larger body, is a matter for debate. At any rate, they exist, and Saturn has often been described as the most beautiful object in the entire universe. With the naked eye it looks like a bright, rather yellowish star.

Titan, the senior satellite of Saturn, is over 3000 miles in diameter, and has a dense, nitrogen-rich atmosphere. However, the atmosphere also contains large amounts of the poisonous gas methane, and this, together with the

Saturn, imaged from Voyager 2 in 1981. Note the shadows of the disk on the rings, and the rings on the disk. Courtesy NASA/JPL-Caltech.

very low temperature, seems to rule out any form of life of the kind we can understand. Four icy satellites (Rhea, Iapetus, Dione and Tethys) are between 600 and 1000 miles across; all the rest are much smaller. By now Saturn has been bypassed by several space-craft, and as I write these words (August 2004) the latest of these, Cassini, is in orbit around Saturn. It carries a smaller probe, Huygens, which is due to be separated from the main craft, and to make a controlled landing on Titan in January 2005.

The two outer giants, ***Uranus*** and ***Neptune***, seem puny in comparison with Jupiter and Saturn, even though they are much larger and more massive than the

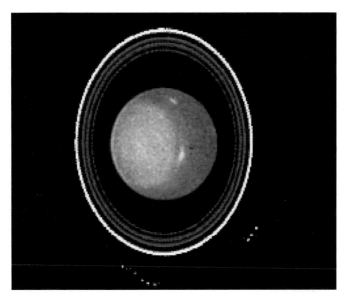

Uranus. Hubble Space Telescope, 14 August 1994 from a range of 1.7 thousand million miles. The rings are clearly shown. Courtesy Kenneth Seidelmann, U.S. Naval Observatory, and NASA.

Earth. Uranus is just visible with the naked eye if you know where to look for it, and binoculars will show Neptune with no difficulty at all.

As a pair, Uranus and Neptune differ markedly from Jupiter and Saturn. It is better to call them ice-giants rather than gas-giants, because they are made up largely of icy materials, though in all probability they do have solid cores. Their atmospheres are, predictably, rich in hydrogen. Both have obscure ring systems, and both have satellite families, though all these are smaller than the four main moons of Jupiter, and Titan in Saturn's system.

Most of what we know about the outer worlds comes

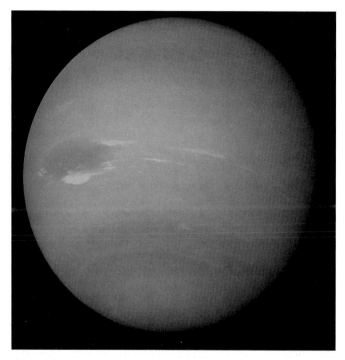

Neptune, from Voyager 2 in 1989. The Great Dark Spot is well shown, but later observations from the Hubble Space Telescope (in the 1990s) showed that it had disappeared.

from one space-craft, Voyager 2, which was launched in 1977 and sent on a round trip. By sheer chance the four giants were arranged in a way which made it possible for Voyager 2 to by-pass each in turn; Jupiter in 1979, Saturn in 1981, Uranus in 1986 and finally Neptune in 1989, sending back excellent pictures of each, plus a vast amount of miscellaneous data. Voyager 2 is still in radio contact, but it is leaving the Solar System, and will never

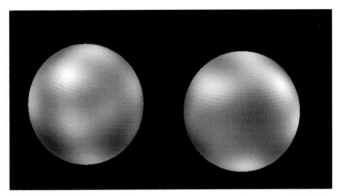

Pluto, imaged from the Hubble Space Telescope in June 1994. The images, taken in blue light, show a certain amount of surface detail. Opposite hemispheres of Pluto are seen in these two views. Courtesy Alan Stern (Southwest Research Institute), Marc Buie (Lowell Observatory), NASA and ESA.

come back. Millions of years hence it may still be wandering between the stars, unseen, unheard and untrackable.

Pluto, discovered less than eighty years ago, is in a different category. It is smaller than the Moon, and has an orbit which is appreciably eccentric and tilted. It has a companion, Charon, whose diameter is more than half that of Pluto itself. Obviously, the Pluto–Charon pair cannot be seen without a reasonably powerful telescope, but the Hubble Space Telescope, orbiting the Earth at over 300 miles above sea-level, has been able to show a few vague markings on Pluto's surface.

Astrologers have apparently had no difficulty in fitting Uranus and Neptune into their general scheme, but Pluto must surely present them with problems. It is satellite-sized rather than planet-sized, and it is not the only body to move in those far-away regions. A great many others have been found during the last ten years, making up what is usually called the Kuiper Belt after the Dutch astronomer Gerard Kuiper, who called attention to it. One member of the swarm, Quaoar, is around 750 miles in diameter, and it has been suggested that Pluto is nothing more than the brightest KBO or Kuiper Belt Object. Sedna, discovered in 2004, is even larger than Quaoar, and has an orbital period of 11,487 years. At its greatest distance from the Sun it recedes to about 80,000 million miles. Also, is there another proper planet well out beyond the Kuiper Belt? There may well be, but if it exists it is bound to be very faint and difficult to locate.

Comets are the most erratic members of the Solar System. They are not massive, solid bodies; a comet is well described as a 'dirty ice-ball', and even a large comet has a nucleus no more than a few miles across. Most comets, though not all, move in very eccentric paths. When they are a long way from the Sun they are inert, icy lumps, but as they move inward and are heated by the Sun's rays they become active; the ices begin to evaporate, so that the comet develops a coma (head) and often a tail or tails, stretching outward. All in all, a comet is an insubstantial object, and I have commented that it is 'the nearest approach to nothing that can still be anything'. Their gravitational pulls are very feeble indeed.

Some comets move in the inner parts of the Solar System, and have short orbital periods – only 3.3 years in the case of Encke's Comet (so named because its movements were first worked out, during the early nineteenth century, by the German astronomer Johann Franz Encke). These short-period comets come from the Kuiper Belt, and all are dim, so that very few ever become visible with the naked eye. Also, they are short-lived by cosmical standards. Every time a comet nears the Sun it loses material to make up the head and the tail, and so it wastes away; several short-period comets seen regularly during the last century have now disintegrated. The only 'regular' comet which can become brilliant is Halley's, which has a period of 76 years. It was last at perihelion in 1986, and will be back once more in 2061. The longest diameter of the peanut-shaped nucleus is less than ten miles, and it would take 60,000 million bodies the mass of Halley's Comet to make one body the mass of the Earth; at each perihelion it loses about 300 million tons of material. Its tail, however, may extend for millions of miles.

Really bright comets come from the Oort Cloud, far beyond the orbits of the known planets. As long ago as 1948 the Dutch astronomer Jan Oort suggested that at a range of several million million miles there might be a swarm of these icy bodies. If one of these objects is perturbed for any reason, it may swing inward and approach the Sun. One of several things may then happen to it. It may simply swing round the Sun and return to the Oort Cloud, not to be seen again for many centuries; it may plunge into the Sun, and be destroyed; it may hit a planet – as Comet Shoemaker–Levy 9 did in 1994, when it impacted Jupiter and caused disturbances in the Jovian atmosphere which persisted for months – or it may be captured by the gravitational pull of a planet, usually Jupiter, and forced into a short-period orbit. The last really conspicuous comet, Hale–Bopp, was a splendid sight in our skies for several months during 1997. It had two main tails, one curved (made up of dust particles) and one straight (made up of gas particles). It will be back around AD 2360, so look out for it then! Its nucleus was about 25 miles across, which by cometary standards is exceptionally large.

As a comet moves along it leaves a dusty trail in its wake. When we pass through one of these trails, many of these particles dash into the upper air. Travelling at anything up to 45 miles per second, they are heated by the friction against the atmospheric particles, and burn away to produce the luminous streaks which we call meteors or shooting-stars. There are many meteor showers per year, notably those of August, when we pass through the trail of Comet Swift–Tuttle, and in November, when we pass through the trail of Comet Tempel–Tuttle. (It is sheer coincidence that the American astronomer Horace Tuttle was the co-discoverer of both these comets.) Meteors are of dust-grain size, and burn away by the time that they have penetrated to a height of about 40 miles above sea-level. Not all are associated with showers; sporadic meteors may appear from any direction at any moment.

Meteorites are quite different. They are not associated with meteors, or with comets; they come from the asteroid belt, and may land intact, often producing craters. Meteorites are either irons, stones or a mixture of both. There is no reliable record of any human casualty due to a falling meteorite, though it is true that several people have had narrow escapes.

Such is the Solar System. In astrology the Sun, Moon and planets are the actors; let us now turn to the stage, provided by the backcloth of the 'fixed stars'.

CHAPTER 4

THE UNIVERSE
OF STARS

It is not always easy to appreciate that the Sun is nothing more than a normal star, and it requires a real mental effort to realise how far away the 'night-time' stars are. The Earth–Sun distance is, as we have noted, 93 million miles. Represent this by one inch, and the nearest star – a faint red star known as Proxima Centauri – will be over four miles away.

Faced with this sort of scale, it is clearly hopeless to use conventional units such as miles and kilometres; it would be as cumbersome as measuring the distance between London and Manchester in inches. Luckily, a more convenient unit is to hand. Light does not travel instantaneously; it flashes along at 186,000 miles per second, so that in one year it covers nearly 6 million

million miles. This distance is called a light-year. Proxima Centauri is 4.2 light-years away; by contrast, light takes only 8.6 minutes to travel from the Sun to the Earth, and a mere one and a quarter seconds to flash from the Earth to the Moon.

The stars make patterns in the sky, known as constellations. I will have more to say about them later, but first let us say something about the stars themselves.

They differ in brightness, partly because they are at different distances from us but also because they differ in real luminosity. Represent the Sun by a candle, and the feeblest stars will be mere glow-worms, while the most powerful stars will be searchlights. A star may look brilliant either because it is close to us on the cosmical scale, because it is genuinely very powerful, or a combination of both. The brightest stars have been given individual names, mainly Arabic. The two most brilliant stars in the sky are Sirius and Canopus. Sirius is the more conspicuous – it is 8.6 light-years away, and 26 times more luminous than the Sun – but Canopus is one of our cosmical searchlights and, according to the Cambridge catalogue, could match 200,000 Suns. In our sky it is outshone by Sirius only because it is 1200 light-years away.

The apparent brightness of a star is given by what is termed apparent magnitude. The scale works the same way as a golfer's handicap: the brightest objects have the lowest magnitudes. Thus a star of magnitude 1 is brighter than a star of magnitude 2, 2 is brighter than 3, and so on. With the naked eye most people can see down to magnitude 6, and modern electronic equipment used with giant telescopes can reach down to magnitude 30. At the other end of the scale, some stars have zero or even minus magnitudes; thus Canopus is –0.7, Sirius –1.5. Of the planets, Venus can achieve –4, and on the same

Cassiopeia, from Bayer's star atlas Uranometria, 1723 edition. Courtesy Royal Astronomical Society.

scale the Sun's magnitude is –26.8.

All stars have catalogue designations. In 1603 the German amateur astronomer Johann Bayer gave Greek letters to the stars in each constellation, beginning with the brightest, Alpha, and working through to Omega, though in practice the alphabetical order is often chaotic. Various other systems are in use, covering many thousands of stars, but only a few of the brightest stars have individual names in common use. (Beware of agencies which claim to be able to give star names, naturally on payment of a sum of money. These agencies are completely bogus.)

Many people believe that all stars look alike, except in magnitude. Nothing could be further from the truth. For example, it is easy to see that the stars differ in colour. The two leaders of Orion, the constellation which dominates the evening skies in winter, bring this out well; Betelgeux (Alpha Orionis) is orange-red, while Rigel (Beta Orionis) is glittering white. Capella, the bright star which is almost overhead as seen from Britain on winter evenings, is yellow, like the Sun, while Vega, which occupies the zenith or overhead position on summer evenings, is steely blue. These colours indicate differences in surface temperature. Red is cooler than yellow, while yellow is cooler than white or blue-ish; thus Betelgeux is cooler than Capella or the Sun, while Rigel is hotter than Capella. Switch on an electric fire, and you will see what I mean; the glowing bars change from red to white as the temperature rises. The Sun's surface is at a temperature of rather less than 6000 degrees Celsius, Betelgeux a mere 3000 degrees, Rigel well over 10,000 degrees.

The nineteenth-century French philosopher August Comte once wrote that mankind could never find out anything definite about the chemistry of the stars. As Iain

Orion, photographed by Michael Maunder. Betelgeux is at top centre, Rigel is the bright star at lower right.

Nicolson has pointed out, this shows that when a French philosopher makes a profound statement he is almost certain to be wrong, and today we have a detailed knowledge of the chemical make-up of the stars. The key instrument is the spectroscope. Just as a telescope collects light, so a spectroscope splits it up, and tells us which substances are contained in the light-source. Most normal stars use hydrogen as 'fuel', but when we come to study stellar evolution we find that the story is decidedly complex.

The Sun began its career by condensing out of a mass of dust and gas known as a nebula (from the Latin word for 'cloud'). As it shrank, under the influence of gravity, it heated up, and when the core temperature had reached around 10 million degrees nuclear reactions began. The Sun's age is of the order of 5000 million years, and it will not change much in the foreseeable future. However, it cannot shine for ever. Eventually, several thousands of millions of years hence, the supply of available hydrogen will run low, and the Sun will change its structure. Different reactions will begin; the interior of the Sun will shrink, while the outer layers will expand and cool, turning the Sun into a red giant star. Next, the outer layers will be thrown off, and what is left of the Sun will be a tiny, amazingly dense star of the type known as a white dwarf. Finally all its light and heat will leave it, and it will become a cold, dead globe. It is not an inviting prospect, but we will not be there to see; the Earth cannot possibly survive when the Sun swells out to become a red giant.

A star of much lower mass than the Sun will never trigger off nuclear reactions, and will simply shine feebly for an immense period before dying. However, some stars are initially much more massive than the Sun, and these run through their evolutionary sequence much more quickly. Rigel, which is about 60,000 times as luminous as the Sun, is using up its hydrogen at an amazing rate, and its luminous career will be cosmically brief. When a very massive star runs out of 'fuel' it will expand to become a red supergiant, as Betelgeux is now, and then explode, blowing most of its material away into space and leaving a tiny core far more massive even than a white dwarf. You could pack 1000 million tons of this material into a thimble.

The explosion of a star of this mass is termed a supernova outburst. Supernovæ are rare – the last to be seen in our Milky Way system flared up as long ago as 1604 – but they are often seen in other galaxies. I mention supernovæ here because it has often been suggested that the Star of Bethlehem may have been due to an outburst of this kind. I am quite sure that this is not so, but I will not go into detail, because I have done so elsewhere – see my book *The Star of Bethlehem* (Canopus Publishing, Bristol, 2001). Needless to say, the Star of Bethlehem remains of great interest to astrologers as well as astronomers!

In an even more extreme case, the old star may become so small and so dense that it will pull strongly enough to prevent even light from escaping from it. It will cut itself off from the rest of the universe, and will create a black hole. Black holes are certainly the most bizarre objects imaginable, but they have nothing to do with astrology, and so they do not concern us here.

Now let me return to the constellations. The first thing to bear in mind is that a 'constellation' means nothing at all, because the stars are at very different distances from us, and we are dealing with nothing more significant than line-of-sight effects. Consider Betelgeux and Rigel, the two leaders of Orion. According to the authoritative Cambridge catalogue, Betelgeux is 310 light-years away from us, while Rigel lies at 900 light-years. There is absolutely no connection between the two, and in fact

Rigel is much further away from Betelgeux than we are. If we were observing from a different vantage point in space, Betelgeux and Rigel could well be on opposite sides of the sky.

The constellation names and boundaries are therefore completely arbitrary, and we can give what names we like. However, the patterns themselves remain virtually the same over periods of many lifetimes. Go back to the time of King Canute, or Julius Cæsar, or even Tutankhamen, and you would see the constellations to all intents and purposes the same as they are now. The stars are not fixed in space; they are moving in all sorts of directions at all sorts of speeds, but they are so far away that their individual or 'proper' motions are very slight. The star with the greatest known proper motion, a dim red dwarf known as Barnard's Star, takes over 190 years to crawl across the sky by a distance equal to the apparent diameter of the full moon. It is only our near neighbours, the members of the Solar System, which wander about from one constellation to another.

Eventually, of course, the constellations will change. The most famous of all the northern groups is Ursa Major, the Great Bear (the Latin names for the constellations are always used; after all, Latin is still international, though as a spoken language it died out long ago). Ursa Major is made up of a pattern of seven reasonably bright stars. Of these, five are moving through space in the same direction, but the remaining two are not. In, say, 50,000 years' time the pattern will have become distorted, as shown in the diagram, but in historical times the changes in the patterns would have been too gradual to be noticed. Measuring the proper motions of stars means using very accurate equipment.

The constellations in our present-day maps are of Greek

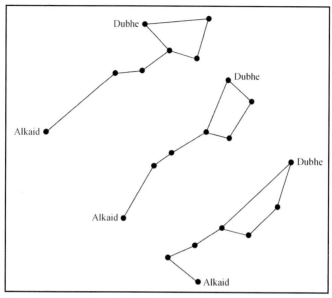

Ursa Major, the Great Bear. Top: 50,000 years ago. Middle: as we see it today. Bottom: as it will appear 50,000 years in the future. Courtesy James Symonds.

origin, at least so far as we know. The last great astronomer of ancient times was Ptolemy of Alexandria (Claudius Ptolemæus), who lived from around AD 120 to 180, and who drew up a star catalogue which was much the best of its time. Ptolemy listed 48 constellations, all of which are to be found on our modern star-maps, though in many cases the boundaries have been modified. New constellations have been added; for example, Ptolemy could never see the stars of the far south, which never rise from the latitude of Alexandria. Ptolemy's constellation names were mainly mythological. For instance, Orion was a great hunter who boasted (wrongly) that he could kill any animal on earth – but he forgot the Scorpion (Scorpius), which crawled out of a hole in the ground, stung him in the heel, and caused his untimely demise. Hercules, Perseus, Andromeda and Cassiopeia are also to be found, as are some birds (Aquila, the Eagle), reptiles (Lacerta, the Lizard) and a few inanimate objects (Lyra, the Lyre or Harp, and Libra, the Balance). Some of the more 'modern' constellations have names of different vintage, such as Telescopium (the Telescope) and Horologium (the Clock).

The constellations show a wide range both in area and in importance. There was a time when every compiler of a new star catalogue felt bound to include constellations of his own, and some of the proposed names were curious, such as Officina Typographica (the Printing Press), and Globus Ærostaticus (the Balloon). Eventually, in the 1930s, the International Astronomical Union – the controlling body of world astronomy – lost patience, and reduced the number of accepted constellations to 88. Among the casualties were Noctua (the Night Owl) and Felis (the Cat). True, neither merited a separate identity, but I for one rather regret the disappearance of the Owl and the Pussycat!

Very few of these constellations give any impression of the figure after which they are named. Try to make the outline of a princess out of the stars in Andromeda, for instance, and I fear that you will fail. Moreover, the constellation boundaries are arbitrary, and during the IAU revision there were some additional changes; several stars were removed from Scorpius and added to Libra, while one bright star, Alnath, was stolen from Auriga (the Charioteer) and given a free transfer to Taurus (the Bull). Even more illogically, one of the stars in the well-marked Square of Pegasus (the Flying Horse) was transferred to

Andromeda. Make what boundaries you like; take your pick!

There is another point which is vitally important in any consideration of astrology. We have to use Ptolemy's system, suitably modified, but other old civilisations did not. For example, the Chinese star-maps include a rat, a tiger, a rooster and a rabbit, while in Egypt our Great Bear becomes the leg of an ox while our Cygnus (the Swan) is a man with the head of a falcon. If we used the Chinese or the Egyptian patterns, our star-maps would look completely different, though of course the stars themselves would be exactly the same.

Come back now to line-of-sight effects, and as an example let us consider Cygnus, one of the most prominent of the northern-hemisphere constellations. Most of it never sets over England, and it is prominent for much of the year, particularly in the summer. There are five main stars, making up an X-pattern, so that Cygnus is often nicknamed the Northern Cross; it is certainly much more cruciform than the Southern Cross (Crux Australis), which is much more like a kite, and which never rises over the British Isles. Here are the essential data of the five main stars of Cygnus:

Greek Letter	Proper Name	Magnitude	Distance (light-years)	Luminosity (Sun = 1)
Alpha	Deneb	1.2	1800	70,000
Beta	Albireo	3.1	390	700
Gamma	Sadr	2.2	750	6000
Delta	–	2.9	160	130
Epsilon	Gienah	2.5	81	60

(Note that Beta Cygni, which ought to be the second

brightest star in the constellation, is almost a magnitude fainter than Gamma; but to make up for this, it is a glorious double star, with a golden-yellow primary and azure-blue companion.)

It is clear that the five stars of the X are in no way associated. Deneb, an exceptionally luminous star, is very much in the background, and a hundred times as remote as Albireo. There is nothing swanlike about Cygnus, and the name, like the constellation itself, is completely meaningless. Now let us turn to the Zodiac, which astrologers regard as being absolutely fundamental to their beliefs.

CHAPTER 5

THE ZODIAC

As a start, note that astrologers depend upon the Zodiacal signs, not the actual constellations – and because of precession, the signs and constellations are now out of step. There is also the problem of Ophiuchus, the Serpent-bearer, a large constellation which intrudes into the Zodiac between Scorpius and Sagittarius. (A small part of Cetus, the Whale, also intrudes.) All the same, astrologers do believe that the names have real significance. Thus Aquarius and Pisces are 'watery' signs, while Leo is masterful and brash.

As we have seen, the Sun's annual path against the stars is known as the ecliptic. The Zodiac extends to either side of the ecliptic, and it is here that the Moon and principal planets are always to be found, simply because their orbits are not sharply inclined to that of the Earth; if you draw a plan of the Solar System on a piece of flat paper, you are not very far wrong. The orbital inclination is 7 degrees for Mercury and less than 4 degrees for all the other planets – apart from Pluto, where the inclination is 17 degrees.

So let us go on a brief 'Zodiac tour', and see what we can find. The main details of the constellations are summarised in the table.

I have included Ophiuchus, which crosses both the ecliptic and the celestial equator, but not Cetus, which does not cross the ecliptic and merely brushes the extreme edge of the Zodiacal band. I have also kept to the usual order, though since Pisces now contains the vernal equinox it should really be classed as the first constellation of the Zodiac rather than the last – and to be strictly logical, the vernal equinox should be re-named the First Point of Pisces! The autumnal equinox, formerly in Libra, is now in Virgo. Neither equinox is marked by any bright star.

Name	English name	Area in square degrees	Stars above Magnitude 2.5
Aries	The Ram	441	Hamal (2.0)
Taurus	The Bull	797	Aldebaran (0.8)
			Alnath (1.6)
Gemini	The Twins	514	Pollux (1.1)
			Castor (1.6)
			Alhena (1.9)
Cancer	The Crab	506	(none)
Leo	The Lion	947	Regelus (1.4)
			Algieba (2.0)
			Denebola (2.1)
Virgo	The Virgin	1294	Spica (1.0)
Libra	The Balance	538	(none)
Scorpius	The Scorpion	497	Antares (1.0)
			Shaula (1.6)
			Sargas (1.9)
			Wei (2.3)
			Dschubba (2.3)
			Girtab (2.4)
Ophiuchus	The Serpent-bearer	948	Rasalhague (2.1)
			Sabik (2.4)
Sagittarius	The Archer	867	Kaus Australis (1.9)
			Nunki (2.0)
Capricornus	The Sea-goat	414	(none)
Aquarius	The Water-bearer	980	(none)
Pisces	The Fishes	889	(none)

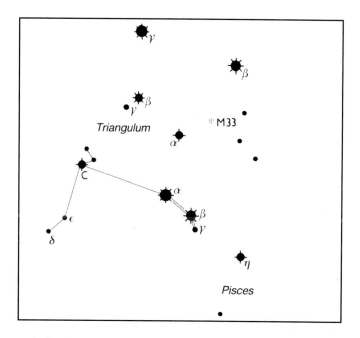

Aries is not very conspicuous, it lies in the general area of Pegasus and Andromeda, and has one brightish star, the orange second-magnitude Hamal. Close by it are two fainter stars; the three lie in a curved line, nothing like the outline of a ram or anything else. In mythology, Aries represents a ram which had a golden fleece, and was able to fly; it rescued two children, Phryxus and Helle, whose father was the King of Thebes. The children were being threatened by their wicked stepmother, so the ram was sent to intervene. Unfortunately Helle lost her balance during the flight, and fell into the sea now called the Hellespunt, but her brother was more fortunate, and arrived safely.

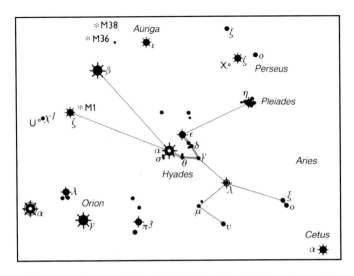

Taurus is one of the brightest of the Zodiacal constellations. Its orange-red leader, Aldebaran (the 'Eye of the Bull'), lies in line with the belt of Orion. Mythologically it represents the bull into which Zeus, ruler of the gods, changed himself in order to carry off Europa, daughter of the King of Crete (the morals of the ancient Olympians were, at best, questionable). Taurus is at its best during winter evenings. It contains two splendid open star-clusters, the Pleiades or Seven Sisters, round the third-magnitude Alcyone, and the Hyades, which extend from Aldebaran. In fact Aldebaran is not a genuine member of the Hyades; it merely lies between the cluster and ourselves – yet another line-of-sight effect.

Taurus has no definite pattern. Remember, too, that its second brightest star, Alnath, used to be included in Auriga, as Gamma Aurigæ; when the IAU revised the constellation boundaries Gamma Aurigæ became Beta Tauri.

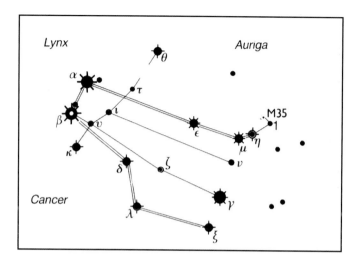

Gemini is a magnificent winter group, crossed by the Milky Way. The twins are Castor and Pollux, sons of the King and Queen of Sparta. Pollux was immortal, but Castor was not. When Castor was killed, Pollux pleaded to be allowed to share his immortality with his brother; his wish was granted, and both boys were placed in the sky. The constellation itself is marked by lines of stars extending from Castor and Pollux in the general direction of Orion.

Pollux is now half a magnitude brighter than its twin, though in some of the old catalogues Castor is recorded as being the leader. Whether there has been any real change is very doubtful. The stars are not alike. Pollux is a single orange star at a distance of 36 light-years; Castor, at 52 light-years, is a complex system made up of two main components, easily separable in a small telescope, and with a much fainter pair nearby.

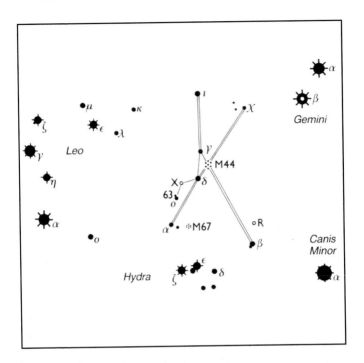

Cancer is one of the least conspicuous of the Zodiacal groups. It lies between Leo and Virgo, and is contained in the large triangle made up of Pollux, Regulus in Leo, and Procyon in Canis Minor (the Little Dog). The brightest star, Beta Cancri or Altarf, is only of magnitude 3.5. The outline of Cancer bears a slight resemblance to a very dim and ghostly Orion. The constellation is redeemed by the presence of the fine naked-eye cluster Præsepe, or the Beehive. In mythology Cancer represents a crab which was sent to attack the hero Hercules. Not unnaturally, Hercules trod on the crab and squashed it.

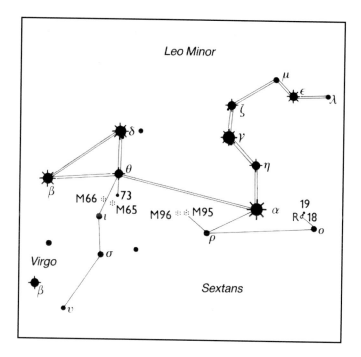

Leo is a large, bright constellation, very prominent during spring evenings. Its leader, the 'Royal Star' Regulus, is of the first magnitude. Extending from Regulus is a curved line of stars, making up a pattern not unlike the mirror image of a question-mark; these make up what is termed the Sickle. The other main stars of Leo – Denebola, Zozma and Chort – form a triangle. With a considerable effort of the imagination it is, I suppose, possible to see the outline of an animal in the Leo pattern, but, as usual, there is no real connection between the stars.

Greek letter	Proper name	Magnitude	Distance (light-years)	Luminosity (Sun = 1)
Alpha	Regulus	1.4	85	130
Gamma	Algieba	2.0	90	60
Beta	Denebola	2.1	39	17
Delta	Zozma	2.6	52	14
Epsilon	Asad Australis	3.0	310	520
Theta	Chort	3.3	78	26
Zeta	Adhafera	3.4	117	50
Eta		3.5	1800	9500
Mu	Rassalas	3.9	96	200

So Eta, which has never been given an individual name, is much the remotest and most powerful of the stars in the main pattern.

Mythologically, Leo represents the Nemæan Lion, killed by Hercules as one of his Labours. Ironically, perhaps, the constellation marking Hercules is not nearly so conspicuous as Leo.

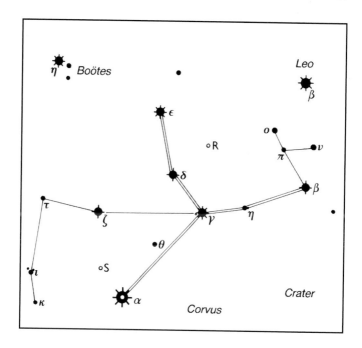

Virgo is one of the largest constellations in the sky; it represents Astræa, the goddess of justice. It is crossed by the celestial equator; the fourth-magnitude Zaniah (Eta Virginis) has a declination of 0 degrees 40 minutes south. Spica is of the first magnitude. The 'bowl' of Virgo contains many galaxies, but all these are too faint to be seen with the naked eye. Gamma Virginis or Arich, in the 'bowl', is a double star, made up of two equal components; the pair can be well separated with a small telescope. Arich is only 36 light-years away, while Spica lies in the background at 260 light-years. It is not difficult to visualise Virgo as a spoon, but certainly not as a virgin!

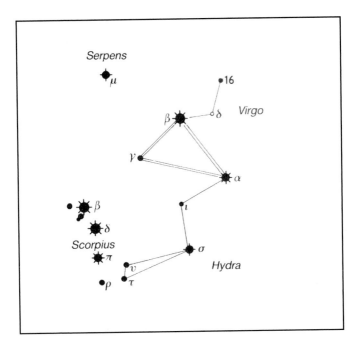

Libra is a very dim constellation, with no distinctive outline; the four main stars make up a distorted quadrilateral. Libra was originally Chelæ Scorpionis, the Scorpion's Claws. It was re-named for no apparent reason; some Greek legends associate it, rather loosely, with Mochis, the inventor of weights and measures.

There is little of immediate interest in Libra. Its brightest star, Beta Libræ or Zubenelchemale, is often said to be the only single naked-eye star which is green in colour, but most people will certainly call it white. Sigma Libræ or Zubenalgubi, of magnitude 3.3, was once included in Scorpius, as Gamma Scorpii.

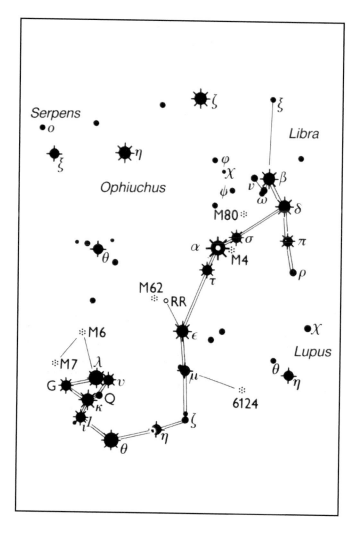

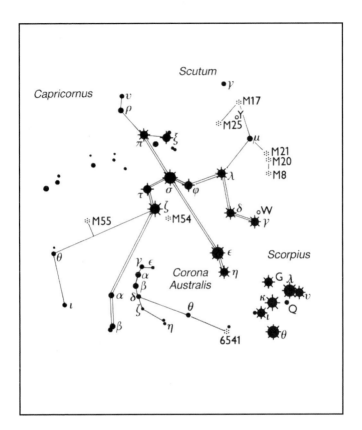

Sagittarius is the southernmost of the Zodiacal constellations; only part of it rises over Britain. Its mythological associations are rather uncertain, and there is no distinctive pattern. Some people liken it to a teapot; at any rate, it is nothing like an archer. Sagittarius contains the lovely star-clouds which hide our view of the centre of the Galaxy, almost 30,000 light-years away.

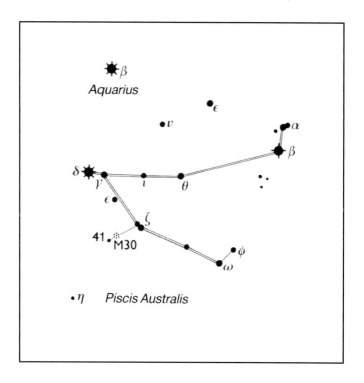

Capricornus has, mythologically, sometimes been linked with the demi-god Pan, but there seems no reason to associate it with a goat, marine or otherwise. It is not at all conspicuous, and has only one star, Deneb Algiedi, above the third magnitude. Alpha Libræ (Al Giedi) is a naked-eye double, but the components are not related; the brighter star is 117 light-years away and 60 times as luminous as the Sun, while the fainter is almost 500 light-years away, with over 5000 times the power of the Sun.

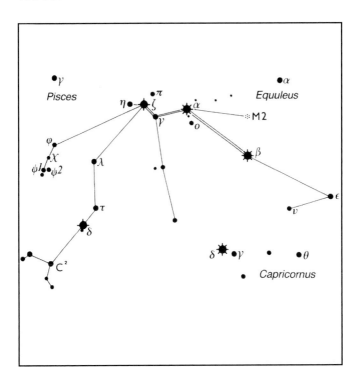

Aquarius is another large, formless and rather barren Zodiacal constellation. There are no well-defined legends attached to it, though it has been associated with Ganymede, the cup-bearer of the gods. There are only two stars above the third magnitude.

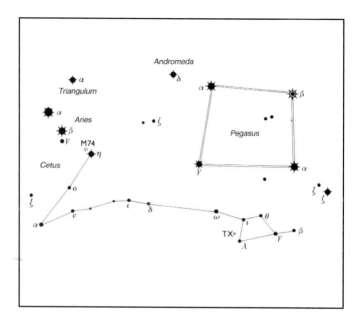

Pisces (bottom) is a faint group, made up chiefly of a long line of dim stars below (south of) the Square of Pegasus. It represents the fishes into which Venus and Cupid once changed themselves in order to escape the unwelcome attentions of the monster Typhon. As a constellation, Pisces is entirely unremarkable.

Such are the twelve constellations of the Zodiac – thirteen, if you include Ophiuchus. As you can see, their outlines are in general very vague, and the names have no significance. Few have even a passing resemblance to the outlines of the objects or people after whom they are named. I suppose one can make out some sort of a case for Gemini, Leo, Scorpius and Pisces, but certainly not for the rest.

We happen to use the Greek Zodiac. We might as well have used the Chinese or the Egyptian, since none of the names given to the chance patterns have any real meaning. So why not create a totally new Zodiac, using the same stars but giving a decidedly modern system of nomenclature? Here, for instance, is my own scheme. The Latinised names have to be rather arbitrary (there were no air-raid sirens or coffee-grinders in Ptolemy's day!) but I have done my best to make the names as appropriate as possible. I have noted the brightest stars, with their conventional names and magnitudes.

Name	English Name	Classical Equivalent
Cochlea Piscatoris	The Fish-slice	Aries
Vehiculum Gravimercale Se Complicans	The Articulated Lorry	Taurus
Vacca Volitans	The Flying Cow	Gemini
Umbra	The Ghost	Cancer
Homo Nivalis Vere, Vere Horribilis	The Abominable Snowman	Leo
Supellex Cubiculii	The Bedroom Utensil	Virgo
Fabarum Conteritor	The Coffee Grinder	Libra
Lacerta Tonutrualis	The Brontosaurus	Scorpius
Instrumentum Quod Se In Mechanicum Insertit	The Spanner	Ophiuchus
Antilia Gasolina	The Petrol Pump	Sagittarius
Porcus Terrestris	The Aardvark	Capricornus
Incursionis Ululator Aeriæ	The Air-raid Siren	Aquarius
Pedeulanum Anarostrum Gravimercale	The Duck-billed Platypus	Pisces

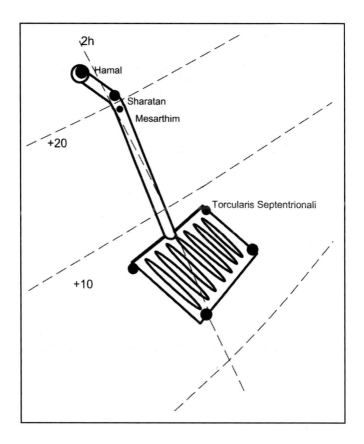

Cochlea Piscatoris Much more like a fish-slice than a ram! It includes the whole of the classical Aries, and extends into part of the adjoining Pisces. The brightest star is Hamal (Alpha Arietis), magnitude 2. If you want to make up a legend about it, why not associate it with the device given to the Japanese fish-god Sushi?

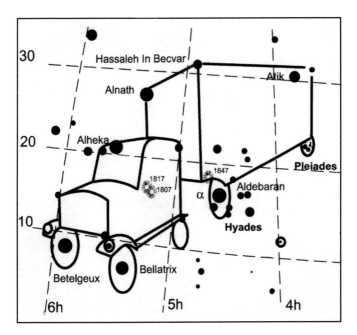

Vehiculum Gravimercale Se Complicans Taurus, with small parts of Orion and Auriga. The front wheels are marked be Betelgeux and Bellatrix, and other wheels by Aldebaran, the Pleiades, Alnath (Beta Tauri) and Hasseleh (Iota Aurigæ).

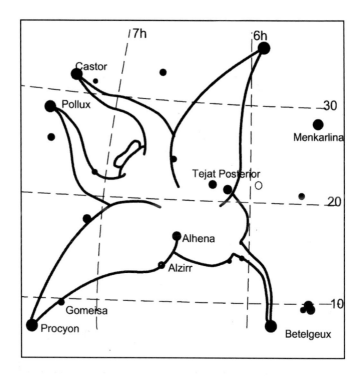

Vacca Volitans The classical sky includes a flying horse (Pegasus), so why not a flying cow? It replaces Gemini; the horns of the cow are marked by Castor and Pollux, while the tail stretches across to Betelgeux in Orion, thus linking the Cow with the Articulated Lorry. It is unwise to loiter underneath this constellation!

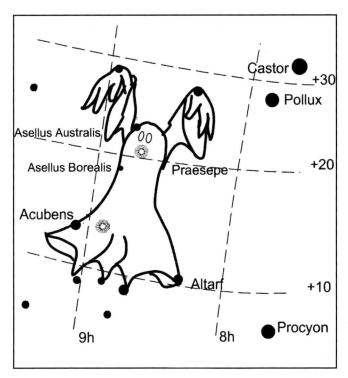

Umbra As wraithlike as the classical Cancer, and it is not easy to improve upon the old legend. Slight mist will hide all the stars in the constellation; only Beta Cancri (Altarf) and Alpha Cancri (Acubens) are above the fourth magnitude.

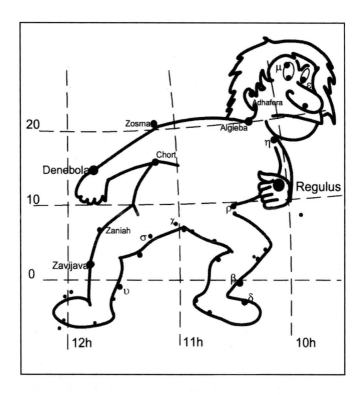

Homo Nivalis Vere, Vere Horribilis The Abominable
Snowman is just as ferocious as the classical Lion. His two
hands are marked by Regulus and Denebola, and his head
replaces the northern part of the classical Sickle. One of
his legs extends into Virgo.

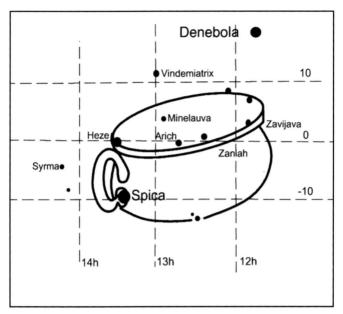

Supellex Cubiculii This is a very obvious pattern, and it is clear that the outline is more like a bedroom utensil than a virgin. Spica makes the handle, the bowl is linked with the leg of the Abominable Snowman by Zaniah (Eta Virginis) and Zavijava (Beta Virginis), both above the fourth magnitude.

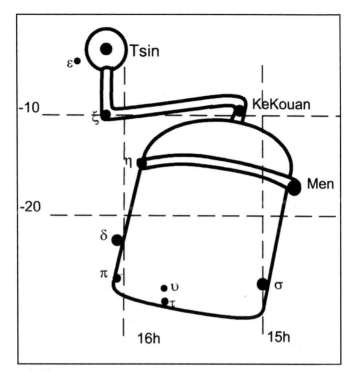

Fabarum Conteritor Another ill-defined constellation with no bright stars. The northernmost star of the pattern is the allegedly green Beta Libræ (Zubenelchemale). With an effort of the imagination, an old-fashioned coffee-grinder can be made out.

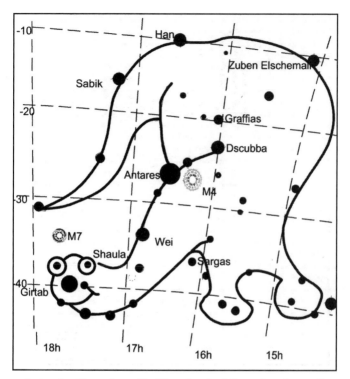

Lacerta Tonutrualis The classical Scorpius; here, the
red Antares marks the neck of the Brontosaurus, and the
head replaces the Scorpion's sting, with the bright Shaula
(Lambda Scorpii).

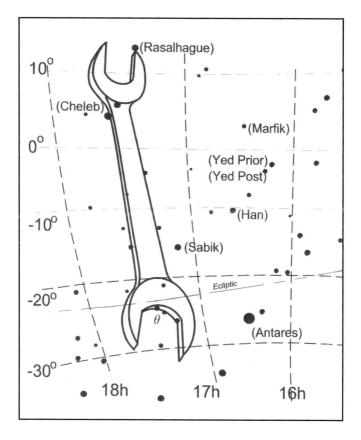

Instrumentum Quod Se In Mechanicum Insertit

This section of Ophiuchus contains one fairly bright star, Theta Ophiuchi, which has no individual name. The name of the group is surely appropriate because astrologers always feel that it throws a spanner into the works!

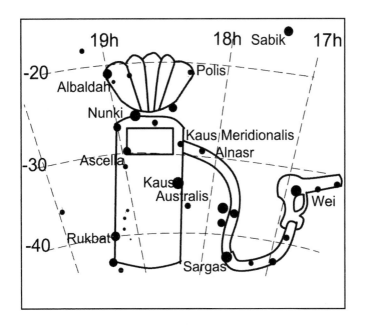

Antilia Gasolina Resembles a petrol pump as adequately as an archer. The main container is well marked, with Kaus Australis (Epsilon Sagittarii) only just below the first magnitude. All of Sagittarius is included, and the hose extends into the classical Scorpius; Sargas is Theta Scorpii.

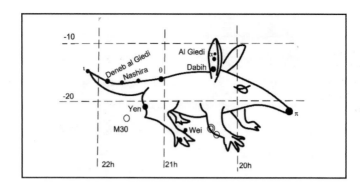

Porcus Terrestris An aardvark is surely more credible than a marine goat. The tail is marked by the brightest star, Deneb al Giedi (Delta Capricorni).

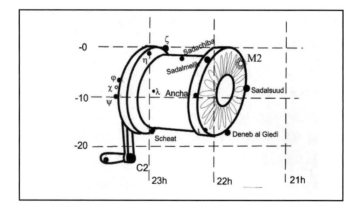

Incursionis Ululator Æriæ This looks more like an air-raid siren than a waterman, assuming that it looks like anything at all. The brightest stars are of the third magnitude.

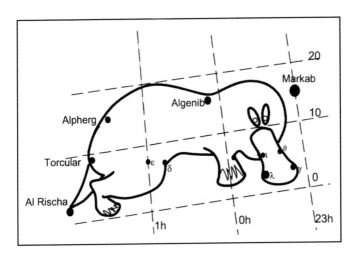

Pedeulanium Anarostrum Gravimercale The classical Pisces; it is doubtful whether the star-gazer who drew up the classical constellations had ever heard of a platypus, duck-billed or otherwise. The only bright stars in the Platypus have been filched from Pegasus; Algenib is Gamma Pegasi, in the Square, while Markab is Alpha Pegasi.

Well – do any of these names seem less suitable than Ptolemy's? The Spanner is there because it intrudes into the Zodiac and upsets the astrological pattern. Virgo is much more reminiscent of a bedroom utensil than a virgin. Sagittarius resembles a petrol pump just as much as a teapot and much more than an archer. Pisces could well be a duck-billed platypus rather than a pair of fishes, while Aquarius, whose outline does not really conjure up any picture at all, could make an air-raid siren just as easily as a man with a watering-pot. Umbra, our Cancer, is there because the area is so dim and starless; the glimmering form of the cluster Præsepe gives it a somewhat ethereal aspect.

All this may seem flippant, and of course it is, but there is an underlying seriousness about it. *These names are just as relevant as Ptolemy's; they mean no more and no less.* Castor and Pollux, our Alpha and Beta Geminorum, could just as easily be Alpha and Beta Vaccæ Volitans; Antares could be Alpha Lacertæ Tonutrualis.

As I write these words (July 2003), Mars is in our Aquarius, while Saturn is in Taurus, near Aldebaran, and Uranus is in Capricornus. We might just as well say that Mars is in the Petrol Pump, Saturn is in the Articulated Lorry, while Uranus shines down coyly among the stars of the Aardvark.

Would new-age astrologers feel, as their predecessors did, that these names have a real significance? Would people born under Antilia Gasolina become captains of industry, would those born under Umbra have psychic gifts, would those born under Fabarum Conteritor be particularly good with their hands, and would those born under Vacca Volitans have to take special care about their personal hygiene? I do not pretend to know, but ideas of this sort are surely worthy of serious consideration from an astrological point of view!

CHAPTER 6

A QUESTION OF GRAVITY

Astrologers maintain that the Sun, Moon and planets have significant effects upon human behaviour. Of course, this is obvious in the cases of the Sun and the Moon, but not for the planets. The first thing we have to decide is whether there can be any scientific explanation for these alleged planetary effects. Can gravitational or magnetic forces be involved? Once we bring in the Zodiacal signs and constellations, we are leaving astronomy and dealing only with astrology, so for the moment let us keep to conventional science.

We depend entirely upon the Sun, and it is the Sun's gravitational pull which keeps the Earth in its orbit. There is no need to go any further down this road, except to add that for a very long time the Sun has shone much as it does today. I have mentioned the Ice Ages, and certainly there have been marked climatic fluctuations even in historic times; for example, between AD 1645 and 1715 there were almost no sunspots; the solar cycle was apparently suspended, and this coincided with a very cold period, at least over Europe. In England, the Thames froze every winter during the 1680s, and frost fairs were held on it; there was talk of evacuating Iceland altogether. Then, around 1715, the spots returned, the so-called 'Maunder Minimum' ended, and the world warmed up. (As an aside, we now hear a great deal about global warming, and it has been suggested that we are responsible, by releasing 'greenhouse gases' into the atmosphere. I admit to being highly sceptical about our involvement, and I put the fluctuations in temperature down entirely to the Sun, but I have to agree that the jury is still out.)

The last major Ice Age ended 10,000 years ago. If the Sun did show marked changes, then life on Earth would become difficult or perhaps impossible. This is bound to happen eventually, but not for at least 1000 million years in the future.

The other body which has profound effects upon life here is the Moon, simply because it is so close to us. Its mean distance from us is less than a quarter of a million miles, and the nearest planet, Venus, is always at least a hundred times as far away. The Moon is the main controller of the tides, and the importance of these cannot be over-estimated. All aquatic life is tidally linked, and so, in many ways, are we. But this again is astronomy, not astrology, and there is no mystery about it. It is widely believed that the phases of the Moon affect human behaviour, and that mentally disturbed people are at their worst when the Moon is full, but even if there is anything in this idea it cannot be associated with gravity, because the phases are not linked with the Moon's changing distance from Earth; the Moon is not necessarily at its closest at the time of full.

(I once studied *Hansard*, the official record of the House of Commons, to see whether the debates were any more irrational at the time of full moon. Unfortunately I found that the general standard of debating was so low that no conclusions could be drawn. However, it is true that the famous House of Lords debate about flying saucers did take place near the time of full moon. In politics, the Newcastle branch of the Green Party took action in 1997. With the solemnity of the truly barmy, they announced that in future they would meet at new moon to discuss ideas, and at full moon to act upon them!)

It is worth noting that we might not be here if the Earth had no moon. It is lunar gravity that keeps the Earth's axis pointing in much the same direction; precession means that there are slight changes, but only for a few degrees to either side of the present 23.5 degrees to the orbital plane. Without the stabilising influence of the Moon, the changes in the tilt of the Earth's axis would be much greater, leading to a very variable and uncomfortable climate. This really does happen on Mars, whose two midget satellites, Phobos and Deimos, are too small to have any detectable effects; the tilt of the Martian axis varies between 35 degrees and only 13 degrees over a period of less than 100,000 years.

So much for the Sun and the Moon. Now let us turn to the planets.

Of course they do cause minor perturbations in the Earth's orbit, but their tidal pulls upon us are negligible compared with those of the Sun and the Moon. The two most massive planets are Jupiter and Saturn, but even

Jupiter has only 1/1047 of the mass of the Sun; of the rest, only Saturn is really worth considering at all, though Venus has also to be reckoned with because it is comparatively nearby. In 1981 L.G. Thompson worked out the relative tidal forces exerted on the Earth by the various planets. Taking the Sun's tidal force as being equal to 1, he gave the following values:

- Venus, 0.000113.
- Jupiter, 0.0000131.
- Mars, 0.0000023.
- Mercury, 0.0000007.
- Saturn, 0.0000005
- Uranus, 0.000000001.
- Neptune, 0.000000002.
- Pluto, 0.0000000000001.

On this scale, the Moon's pull is 2.1.

These values may need some revision, particularly the case of Pluto, which now seems to be nothing more than the largest member of the Kuiper Belt. In any case, its pull on us is certainly less than that of Ceres, the senior member of the main belt of asteroids lying between the orbits of Mars and Jupiter. Ceres has more than one-third the diameter of Pluto, and is a great deal closer.

For all practical purposes, the gravitational effects of the planets can be neglected. But suppose several planets act together? Could this make any difference?

As the planets move round the Sun at different distances and at different speeds, they must sometimes line up, at least approximately, so that they appear close together in the sky even though they are really a very long way apart, with one planet in the background, so to speak. When two planets are involved, the phenomenon is called a conjunction; if three or more planets take part, we have what is termed a planetary massing. For example, on 14 September, 1186, all five naked-eye planets were spread along an arc of less than 12 degrees, with the Sun only a few degrees away; this led to one of the earliest end-of-the-world scares, with predictions of storms, fires, whirlwinds and earthquakes – none of which materialised. There was a similar massing on 19 February, 1524, and this time vast floods were forecast; again, nothing happened. It might be thought that alarms of this sort belong to the past – but not so. The latest scare dates back only to 1982, with the notorious 'Jupiter effect'. This was not a visible massing, but it was claimed that all the planets (or most of them) would be pulling in the same direction, with marked effects on the Sun and dire results for the Earth.

The scare was started by a book, *The Jupiter Effect*, by two British science writers, John Gribbin and Stephen Plagemann. They stated that between 1977 and 1982 the main planets would be aligned in a pattern which occurs only once in 179 years, and they went on to describe a depressing sequence of events. The combined gravitational pulls of the planets would stretch out the Sun; this would cause vast disturbances on the solar surface, and these disturbed areas would shoot out electrified particles, many of which would strike the Earth, changing its rate of rotation. This change would cause strains in the Earth's globe, triggering off earthquakes along lines of weakness in the crust, such as the famous San Andreas Fault in the United States, which passes near San Francisco. All sorts of unpleasant effects would follow.

The book was cleverly written, and was well publicised.

A programme at the London Planetarium, *Omens*, did not help; it was dramatic, and really frightened quite a number of people before I persuaded the Planetarium authorities to take it off. I lost count of the number of letters I had to write about the affair; the Royal Astronomical Society felt bound to issue an official statement, and I put on a special *Sky at Night* television programme. The scare spread to the United States and various countries in Europe, and took months to die down.

Needless to say, there were no earthquakes or effects of any kind, and a few moments' thought ought to have been enough to show the absurdity of the whole idea. The tidal stretching of the Sun could not amount to more than a few millimetres at most, which is not much when you remember that the Sun is 865,000 miles in diameter; moreover, we know that the solar surface pulsates up and down to the extent of about six miles in periods ranging from several minutes to several hours, which is more than enough to mask any planetary effects. The maximum planetary tides on the Sun are 2.7 million times weaker than the Moon's tidal effects upon the Earth.

Moreover, Gribbin and Plagemann claimed that comparable alignments occur every 179 years, so it is possible to make a check. Take 179 away from 1982, and we have 1803; there were no major earthquakes anywhere near that date. Subtract another 179, and we reach 1624; again, there is no evidence of unusual seismic activity. The Sun is to some extent a variable star, and there is maximum activity every 11 years or so, with many sunspots and flares. Gribbin and Plagemann predicted that the planetary alignment would delay solar maximum from 1980, when it was due, until 1982. It didn't.

Predictably, some Biblical sects became highly vocal,

and went so far as to forecast the Second Coming. I have in my possession a pamphlet from Coleraine, in Ireland, which pulled no punches. 'There will be weird lighting effects from the northern lights as they burst through the sky repeatedly. ... The wind directions will completely change. ... The Earth's rotation will be graphically affected and the length of our days will be changed. There will be massive storms on our Earth. ...' and so on. Actually, 1982 was a fairly placid year from a meteorological point of view.

Planetary massings and alignments are not so rare as might be thought. There was an interesting spectacle on the evening of 6 April, 2000, when, as seen from Britain, Jupiter, Saturn, Mars and the crescent moon were all shining down from the western sky. A few hours later, we were treated to a splendid display of aurora – the best for years – though I hasten to add that the aurora had absolutely nothing to do with the planets. The most exact alignment took place on the following 5 May, and involved Venus, Mercury, Jupiter, Mars, Saturn and the Moon, though all were so near the Sun in the sky that nothing unusual could be noticed. The minimum separation was just under 26 degrees, spanning the distance from Mars and the Moon on one side of the Sun, to Venus on the other. This is not at all precise. (Cut a circular cake into 14 equal sectors, and each sector will be just under 26 degrees across.)

Clearly, then, the gravitational pulls of the planets are far too weak to cause any detectable effects upon us. The 'Jupiter effect' is a myth.

It has also been suggested that there may be planetary effects upon the Earth's magnetic field, which in turn could affect us. It does not take much time to rule this out of court. Of our three nearest neighbours, Mars has a magnetic field so weak that it is barely detectable, while Venus and the Moon have no magnetic fields at all. The giant planets do have fields, and that of Jupiter, particularly, is very strong, but they are too remote to have any influence upon the Earth's magnetosphere, i.e. the region round the Earth inside which our magnetic field is dominant.

Having disposed of gravitation and magnetism, it is time for me to turn – at last! – to what must be regarded as 'pure astrology'.

CHAPTER 7

PLANETS, ZODIACS AND SIGNS IN THE SKY

For several months during 2001, in fact for much of the summer, Mars lay in the constellation of Sagittarius, the Archer; it was much the brightest object in that part of the sky, though from countries such as England it was inconveniently low down over the horizon.

Many boys and girls were born during Mars' residence in Sagittarius. Therefore, say the astrologers, these children ought to grow up to be rather boisterous, courageous and sceptical.

But wait! Sagittarius is not a unit; it is merely a chance arrangement of entirely unrelated stars, and the name given to it is quite meaningless. In my Zodiac, Sagittarius becomes Antilia Gasolina, the Petrol Pump. This name is just as valid. In fact, it may even be said that the stars indicate a pump rather more convincingly than they recall an archer.

In my new Zodiac, what would be the characteristics of our new-born baby? Would he or she be endowed with mechanical skill, and perhaps be glad to serve others?

It is equally meaningless to describe a planet as being 'in' a constellation. During the summer of 2001 Mars was roughly 40 million miles away from us, which is equivalent to between 3 and 4 light-minutes. In Sagittarius – or Antilia Gasolina – the brightest stars close to Mars at that time were Nunki, Ascella, Kaus Borealis and Polis, or, to give them their official designations, Sigma, Zeta, Lambda and Mu Sagittarii. Their distances from us are respectively 209, 78, 98 and 3900 light-years, and it is clear that Polis is a real searchlight, outshining our Sun by a factor of 60,000. Saying that Mars was 'in' Sagittarius is as illogical as claiming that if you take a cricket ball and hold it at arm's-length against a cloud background, the ball is 'in' the clouds.

To me, at least, the idea that a small, non-luminous, nearby planet could affect us by its changing position against a random background of stars makes no sense at all. It is only fair to add that the astrologers who really believe what they are saying concentrate not on the actual constellations, but on the Zodiacal signs, which are now out of step – and the sign of an obscure constellation such as Libra is regarded as just as important as the sign of a brilliant group, such as Scorpius or Gemini.

There is also the problem of Ophiuchus and Cetus, both of which invade the Zodiac. Ophiuchus is the more prominent of the two so far as the astrologers are concerned, and some years ago a misleading broadcast by a professional astronomer seemed to claim that a new Zodiacal constellation had been discovered! The tabloid press became really excited, until it was pointed out that the situation had been quite clear to Ptolemy and all the other old-time watchers of the sky. Most astrologers now prefer to pretend that Ophiuchus doesn't exist.

Some time ago I had a brief conversation about all this with a Mrs Hone, then President of the Astrological Society. I was bold enough to suggest that astrologers had adopted names for the constellations and then assumed that these names had real significance; for example Aquarius was taken to be a 'watery' sign (in my Zodiac, however, it has been transformed into an air-raid siren). Mrs Hone did not agree, and also pointed out that no horoscope can be infallible, as the essential data are rarely complete. In fact, one cannot cast a horoscope and then deduce from it that the person concerned is left-handed, used to be snooker champion of East Grinstead, dislikes asparagus and has a maiden aunt in Hoxton. One must not expect too much.

What about unusual celestial phenomena, such as supernovæ, eclipses and comets? I have already said a little about them from an astronomical point of view, but once again we find we are walking along a blind alley.

Supernovæ are colossal outbursts, marking the death-throws of a very massive star. One blazed out in 1572 in the constellation of Cassiopeia, and I cannot resist quoting the account of it given by Tycho Brahe, of Denmark, one of the greatest characters in the history of astronomy, and compiler of the most accurate star-catalogue of pre-telescopic times: 'The star was at first like Venus and Jupiter, giving pleasing effects; but as it then became like Mars, there will next come a period of wars, seditions, captivity and death of princes, and destruction of cities, together with dryness and fiery meteors in the air, pestilence, and venomous snakes. Lastly the star will become like Saturn, and there will finally come a time of want, death, imprisonment and all sorts of sad things.'

However, the supernova was rather too remote to cause any alarm; its distance from us was a full 8000 light-years. It faded; after less than two years it had become visible with the naked eye, and its remnant is now extremely dim. It is true that if a supernova flared up within a few light-years of us there could be problems, but the chances of this are infinitesimal.

Lunar eclipses, when the Moon passes into the shadow cast by the Earth, are gentle and beautiful phenomena, and astrologers do not pay much attention to them. However, one lunar eclipse altered the course of history. In 413 BC the Peloponnesian War was raging in Greece, between Athens and Sparta, and the Athenian expeditionary force that had invaded Sicily was in serious trouble. It could have escaped by sea, but an eclipse of the Moon was due, and the astrologers persuaded the Athenian commander, Nicias, to delay evacuation 'for thrice nine days'. By that time it was too late; the escape route was blocked, and the entire Athenian force was wiped out. It was this that led directly to the defeat of Athens in the war.

A total eclipse of the Sun is a very different matter, and it is not surprising that early peoples were alarmed by them. However, at a total eclipse the drop in temperature is very temporary, and there are no long-term effects at all. The difference in position between a new moon which produces an eclipse and a new moon which does not produce an eclipse is only a few degrees. Astrologers in Britain were predictably vocal in August 1999, when the track of totality crossed Cornwall and Devon, and were disappointed when nothing untoward happened. No doubt they will be equally disappointed at the time of

Solar eclipse, taken by Christopher Doherty on 24th October 1995, from a boat on the South China seas.

the next Cornish total eclipse, on 23 September 2090.

Finally we must consider comets, which astrologers have always regarded as unlucky. Remember the lines in Shakespeare's *Julius Cæsar*:

> When beggars die, there are no comets seen:
> The heavens themselves blaze forth the death of princes.

The only bright comet which comes back regularly is Halley's. When it returned in 1910 there was widespread alarm, mainly because a French astronomer had been incautious enough to point out that a comet's tail contains poisonous gases – and that on this occasion the Earth would pass through the tip of the tail. What he neglected to say was that the density of a comet's tail is so low that it could have no effect upon anything; the density is in fact millions of times less than that of our air at sea-level. All the same, many people in America sealed their windows at the time when the comet made its closest approach to the Earth, the idea being to keep out the noxious fumes, and the astrologers made all sorts of dire predictions.

In 1973 Kohoutek's Comet was expected to become brilliant (though in the event it failed to do so), and the astrologers were in full cry. For instance there was a lurid pamphlet, The Christmas Monster, written by a Mr Moses David, who decreed that the comet was a sign of divine vengeance. There would, he said, be widespread damage, with storms, tempests and violent earthquakes, coupled with the downfall of Fascist America and its new Nazi Emperor (whoever that may have been).

When Halley returned once more, in 1986, there were renewed fears, and I remember seeing one London parade whose leaders were proclaiming that the end of the world was nigh. In 1997 Comet Hale–Bopp was on view, and in

March over thirty members of a strange religious cult committed suicide, apparently convinced that they would be transported to Heaven in a spaceship travelling in the wake of the comet.

Is there any scientific justification for these fears? We have to admit that a cometary impact would cause wide devastation, and it can happen. In 1908 a body from Outer Space hit Siberia, blowing pine trees flat over a wide area; the exact nature of the object is not known – it may have been a meteorite, or the icy fragment of a comet – but if it had landed in a city the death-toll would have been colossal. In 2001 the British Government set up a committee to investigate the whole problem of cometary or asteroid impacts, and in the United States there are astronomers constantly on the look-out for potentially dangerous impactors, but this has nothing to do with astrology.

Bear in mind that a comet has a very feeble pull of gravity, and can have no influence upon the Earth unless there is an actual collision. The late Sir Fred Hoyle and his colleagues have proposed that life on Earth was originally brought here via a comet, and that even today comets may drop disease-producing viruses into our upper air, but medical men in general seem to be decidedly unimpressed. I do not propose to say more, because my ignorance of medical matters is fairly complete, but in any case it is not relevant, because it too has no connection with astrology of any kind.

Let me now turn to the most important question of all. Scientifically based or not, does astrology work?

CHAPTER 8

ANALYSIS

We have discussed the 'Jupiter effect'. Now we have the 'Mars effect', due to the researches of a French astrologer, Michel Gauquelin, and his former wife Françoise. They have maintained that Mars occupies certain positions in the sky more often during the birth of sports champions than at the birth of less distinguished people. Of course, defining a sports champion is bound to be somewhat arbitrary; one cannot dispute the claims of Tiger Woods or Shane Warne, but lower down the scale things become a little blurred. One has to use one's own judgement.

The path in the sky along which Mars travels from rising to setting is astrologically divided into six equal parts or sectors, with another six sectors for the time when Mars is below the horizon. According to the Gauquelins, the key sectors are 1 and 4; if Mars lies in one of these when your child is born, he or she may look forward to a sporting career. However, this effect seems to work only for Mars, not for the Sun or Moon or the other planets, so that the initial failure rate is rather high. Again, the only possible scientific explanations for such an effect are gravitational and magnetic, which we have already ruled out. Incidentally, it must be added that after years of marriage the Gauquelins divorced. Evidently their star-signs were not compatible, but as professional astrologers they should surely have realised this before their wedding day!

So far as the star-signs are concerned, each is said by astrologers to have definite significance, but there are problems here. I happen to have been born on 4 March, at ten o'clock in the morning GMT; will another boy born at the same time be anything like me in character and personality? Scientifically there would be no reason why there should be any resemblance. Moreover, what about twins? I know twin boys who were born within ten minutes of each other. One is a musician, the other an engineer, one is tall and muscular, the other slight of build. In every way they could not be less alike.

Looking up some facts in a well-known book on astrology, I found that people born under the sign of Leo were liable to be magnanimous, generous and broad-minded, but this does not really seem to apply to the late Benito Mussolini, whose birthday was 29 July. Checking on the star-signs of famous people, both past and present, can be fun, and of course in some cases the fit is excellent, but it must be said that astrologers are expert in the art of coincidence-hunting, even though I am quite sure that may of them do not realise it.

My next step was to carry out an analysis of my own, using the conventional Zodiacal signs. These are:

Aries	21 March – 20 April
Taurus	21 April – 21 May
Gemini	22 May – 21 June
Cancer	22 June – 22 July
Leo	23 July – 23 August
Virgo	24 August – 23 September
Libra	24 September – 23 October
Scorpio	24 October – 22 November
Sagittarius	23 November – 21 December
Capricornus	22 December – 20 January
Aquarius	21 January – 19 February
Pisces	20 February – 20 March

I worked out a questionnaire, and then set out to find people who would help. This was not difficult. I wanted a cross-section, so I distributed my forms at meetings of various kinds; the local paper – the *Chichester Observer* – printed the forms, and I had hundreds of replies. The questions covered a wide range:

1. Do you play any musical instrument to a reasonable standard?
2. Are you mechanical? (For example, could you carry out simple car maintenance?)
3. Do you like beetroot?
4. Do you play (or have you played) any team game, such as cricket, tennis or football, on a regular basis?
5. Do you have any official qualification in science?
6. Do you have any official qualification in teaching?
7. Have you any interest in military matters? For example, would you ever consider joining the Armed Forces?

8   Can you speak any foreign language fairly fluently?
9   Can you paint or draw to a reasonable standard?
10 Do you enjoy foreign travel?
11 Do you play chess to a reasonable standard?
12 Have you won any awards for sporting prowess?

At the outset I had no idea what I was going to find, if anything. I remember commenting that if the analysis proved that practically everyone born under Gemini liked beetroot, while practically everyone born under Capricornus hated it, I would have to do some radical re-thinking. At any rate, here are the results.

Altogether, 540 people took part. All in all, the results were fairly random, but there were one or two very interesting exceptions. For example, 45 per cent of people born in the sign of Leo could play a musical instrument with fair competence, but for Pisces the percentage was much lower – only 15. Aries provided the highest percentage of qualified teachers (35 per cent) as against almost none for Aquarius and very few for Taurus. Libra favoured chess players (50 per cent), but Capricornus did not (15 per cent). Sagittarians were beetroot lovers (over 98 per cent), but Cancerians were less keen (50 per cent). Science came out well under Gemini (79 per cent) but very badly under Taurus (16 per cent), even though these two signs are adjacent in the Zodiac. Leo provided the best linguists (50 per cent) and Scorpio the worst (22 per cent). So far as team games were concerned, the extremes were Sagittarius (69 per cent) down to Capricornus (a mere 16 per cent). And while 83 per cent of Librans could carry out simple car maintenance, Pisceans (31 per cent) could not.

Obviously these results are not conclusive, because only 540 people took part, and some of the questions are too vague. Sporting prowess is a case in point. It is not clear where the borderline lies, and it would be difficult to justify the claim of, say, the croquet champion of North Nibley. To give the results in detail would be rather pointless, but it seems worth giving a very brief summary:

Question no.	'Yes' answers	
	Above average	Below average
1	Gemini, Leo, Virgo, Capricornus	Taurus, Libra, Pisces
2	Aries, Libra, Aquarius	Taurus, Scorpio, Pisces
3	Aries, Sagittarius	Cancer
4	Sagittarius, Pisces, Aquarius	Cancer, Capricornus
5	Gemini	Taurus
6	Aries	Pisces, Aquarius, Scorpio
7	Virgo, Aquarius	Scorpio, Gemini
8	Leo, Pisces	Libra
9	Sagittarius, Taurus, Aries	Gemini
10	Sagittarius, Aquarius	Pisces
11	Libra, Gemini	Capricornus
12	Libra, Aries, Taurus	Leo, Cancer, Capricornus

No doubt a different selection of people, and different questions, would yield different results. I do not personally believe that tests of this kind can ever prove anything definite, but make up your own mind!

CHAPTER 9

BEYOND SCIENCE?

At the start of this book I said that I was setting out to see if we could throw any light on just two questions: Does astrology work? And if so, why?

It is, I think, fair to say that most astrological claims can be dismissed out of hand. Comets, eclipses, planetary conjunctions, auroræ ... these are not associated with any detectable effects, either upon the Earth or upon those of us who live on it. Of course some astrological predictions come true, but, as was once said, 'it is impossible to always be wrong', though admittedly some modern politicians do their best. I recall one astrological annual which correctly predicted the murder of President Kennedy. However, in previous years it had also made similar predictions with regard to Winston Churchill,

Mao Tse-tung and General de Gaulle, so that it did not appear to be very reliable.

Scientifically, the only conceivable way in which the planets could affect us is by way of their gravitational or magnetic fields. The most elementary calculations are enough to show the absurdity of this, even when all the planets are pulling in the same direction. It is hard to understand why the Gribbin–Plagemann 'Jupiter effect' was ever taken seriously even by laymen.

Come next to the Zodiacal signs, associated with the arbitrarily-named constellations. Again there can be no possible link, because we are dealing with nothing more significant than totally unrelated stars lying at very different distances from us. There is, however, just one loophole which is worth discussing, and which I have not seen mentioned elsewhere, though I would be the last to claim that my searches of the literature have been exhaustive, and there is much that I am sure I have overlooked.

The Zodiacal signs (or, for that matter, the constellations) are linked with the seasons. So far as the Earth's northern hemisphere is concerned, Scorpius and Sagittarius are summer constellations, while Taurus and Gemini are at their best in the winter. The differences in temperature are very marked in most places in the world – in England, August is a great deal warmer than February. Therefore, can a baby born during the warmth of August be even slightly different physically from a baby who first saw the light of day during a bitter spell in February?

I know nothing about medical matters, and so am not qualified to give an opinion, but I took the trouble to ask for the views of around a dozen doctors and specialists. They all told me that if there were any effects at all, which they doubted, these would be inappreciable. And, of course, our seasons are opposite to those in Australia, while countries such as Singapore have virtually no seasons at all.

In searching for a scientific basis for astrology, we seem to have run up against a blank wall. Yet there are millions of people who believe in it. What explanations can be given by the astrologers themselves?

It is only too easy to talk airily about 'vibrations', cosmic waves, occultism and the like, but this does not get us very far, and when pressed for an opinion most astrologers will simply retreat into a maze of meaningless mumbo-jumbo. But there are exceptions. During a television programme some years ago, I discussed it with a leading professional astrologer, Mrs Julia Parker, whom I know personally, and of whose honesty and integrity there is not the slightest doubt.

When I asked her why, in her view, astrology worked, she said frankly that she did not have the slightest idea. To her, a horoscope was a general guide, to be used in much the same way as a medical diagnosis. She also said that the future of astrology was certain to be independent of astronomy; there had been a final parting of the ways, so that astrologers were much more closely linked with psychologists and psychiatrists. I wondered whether we would ever have a new profession: that of an astrolo-psychiatrist. I doubted it – but in the strange world of AD 2004 I suppose that anything is possible.

Astrology has no scientific basis. This has to be admitted by every rational person. Sufficient juggling with figures, and selective coincidence-hunting, will always persuade some people that there is 'something in it', but this takes us away from the real world into the realm of fantasy. Can you really credit that the position of a tiny planet, seem against a random background of unrelated stars, can have any influence upon your character or destiny?

Perhaps it will be fitting for me to end with a personal reminiscence. One Saturday, some years ago, I was due to play cricket for my local team. I was having a good season with my unorthodox leg-breaks, and from my point of view the weather outlook was favourable. I chanced to look at the astrology column of my daily paper, and found that I was due for an outstanding success on the sports field. Encouraged, I consulted two more papers, with the same result. A friend who was staying with me knew how to cast a horoscope, and he was confident that this would be my best day of the season. In the event, I took no wickets and conceded 56 runs. Evidently something went badly wrong with the lines of cosmic communication!

Will astrology survive? Yes, at least in the short term; it has lasted for thousands of years, and now, as the twenty-first century opens, it shows no signs of decline. Alchemy, that other famous pseudo-science, has to all intents and purposes vanished, and is forgotten by all apart from historians. Eventually, astrology will suffer the same fate – but not yet.

INDEX